ORFF ORCHESTRATIONS

GRADE 4

SERIES AUTHORS

Judy Bond

René Boyer

Margaret Campbelle-Holman

Emily Crocker

Marilyn C. Davidson

Robert de Frece

Virginia Ebinger

Mary Goetze

Betsy M. Henderson

John Jacobson

Michael Jothen

Chris Judah-Lauder

Carol King

Vincent P. Lawrence

Ellen McCullough-Brabson

Janet McMillion

Nancy L.T. Miller

Ivy Rawlins

Susan Snyder

Gilberto D. Soto

Kodály Contributing Consultant
Sr. Lorna Zemke

ACKNOWLEDGMENTS

Grateful acknowledgment is given to the following authors, composers, and publishers. Every effort has been made to trace the ownership of all copyrighted material and to secure the necessary permissions to reprint these selections. In the case of some selections for which acknowledgment is not given, extensive research has failed to locate the copyright holders.

I'll Rise When the Rooster Crows Appalachian Folk Song. Music by Uncle Dave Macon. Copyright © 1983 Butterside Music. International Copyright Secured. All Rights Reserved.

Roll On, Columbia Words by Woody Guthrie. Music based on "Goodnight, Irene" by Huddie Ledbetter and John Lomax. TRO – Copyright © 1936 (Renewed), 1957 (Renewed) and 1963 (Renewed) Ludlow Music, Inc., New York, NY. International Copyright Secured. All Rights Reserved including Public Performance For Profit. Used by Permission.

B

Table of Contents

Introduction

The Orff approach to music education actively involves students in speech, movement, singing, instrument playing, and drama. Developed by the German composer Carl Orff (1895–1982), the approach is based on the instinctive learning behavior of children. Improvisation and movement permeate the learning process, and the use of specially designed Orff instruments enables children to create and perform ensemble music at every level.

The materials used include both folk and composed music, along with chants, rhymes, and poetry. As children experience this music, they develop a musical vocabulary and skills that may then be used to create original works.

Orff orchestrations have been created for selected songs in SPOTLIGHT ON MUSIC. Teaching suggestions are found at **music.mmhschool.com**. They include:

Instrumentation—All parts except timpani are commonly written in the treble clef. Bass xylophone and bass metallophone sound an octave below the written pitch. Soprano xylophone, soprano metallophone, and alto glockenspiel sound an octave above the written pitch. The soprano glockenspiel sounds two octaves above the written pitch. The alto xylophone and alto metallophone sound at the written pitch.

Teaching the Orchestration—A suggested basic teaching sequence is given for each orchestration. In orchestrations, the bass part is usually the most important. Throughout this book, the rhythm pattern is used to accompany a number of songs. This pattern outlines the length of the musical phrase. If children have difficulty playing this pattern while the song is being sung, have them play the bass pitches on the steady quarter-note beat.

NOTE: It is not expected that children will be able to play the accompanying parts while singing the song, although, in some cases, singing the song makes playing easier.

The teacher may also choose to use only some of the suggested parts, depending on circumstances such as ability of student, time available, or the accessibility of specific instruments. Many of the arrangements can be musically satisfying with only the bass part and one other part added for tone color and/or rhythmic interest.

Parts in Orff orchestrations are commonly taught with children mirroring the teacher, using the body as an instrument. The teacher is, therefore, required to perform many motions "backwards." To aid in this process, some directions in this book are given from the teacher's perspective (i.e., right refers to the teacher's right; children will mirror with the left hand).

Opportunities for Creativity/Improvisation—For each song, strategies are outlined which allow children to make musical decisions and/or improvise rhythmically or melodically.

Form—Suggestions for the final form may include introductions, interludes, codas, chants, and opportunities for improvisation.

Noteworthy—This is a list of important musical elements that can be reinforced with the orchestration.

The Orff approach can infuse music classes with a spirit of cooperation and joy, enabling students to develop concentration and perception skills, increased aesthetic awareness and physical coordination, and a high level of motivation.

General Suggestions

1. Teach one pattern at a time. Allow students to take their time in learning each part. They should feel comfortable with singing the song while playing a pattern before adding the next pattern.

2. Teach each pattern through movement, with the song. Have students:

   • Mirror you in doing each new rhythm pattern with body movement—preferably large locomotor movements (walking, jumping)—especially for parts that occur on the beat and/or the strong beat. Others can be done with body percussion patterns you create (clapping, patting and/or stamping) or mirroring you in doing the movements required to play the part on the instrument.

   • Sing the song, doing the pattern in movement.

   • Remove any unused bars on pitched instruments, to make understanding and playing the patterns easier.

   • Form groups of three or four students around any available instruments and take turns playing the pattern. (Later, the pattern can be assigned to the instrument indicated in the score. At this time, you only want to give all the students an opportunity to learn the pattern and to help others in their groups to learn it.)

3. After teaching the most basic part, add other parts one at a time. Have students:

   • Sing the song, watching and listening as you play each new pattern.

   • Form two groups and sing the pitches or say the rhythm of the pattern while doing the pattern in body percussion (or by mirroring you) as the other group sings the song and plays previously learned patterns. Switch roles for the groups and repeat. (Use speech patterns given, or create your own. Patterns occurring only on the beat and strong beat, or on a single note—such as at the ends of phrases—can usually be taught without spoken patterns.)

   • All together, sing the song while doing the pattern in body percussion (or mirroring you).

   Clarify pitches played, or learn about instrument technique as needed. Take turns playing the pattern while singing the song.

4. Relate the accompaniment to the lesson focus. Have students:

   • Recognize and describe ways that the accompaniment connects with and relates to the musical focus of the lesson. (It is important for students to realize what they are learning musically and how playing the accompaniments contributes to this.)

   • Review this connection each time you work on the orchestration.

5. Perform the accompaniment as indicated in the score, or as adapted by you and the students. Have students form groups at each instrument needed and take turns playing each part with the song.

A la puerta del cielo
(At the Gate of Heaven)

Spanish Folk Song
Arranged by Virginia Nylander Ebinger

*shoes

GRADE 4

A la puerta del cielo (page 2)

an - gels who go walk-ing bare - foot. Slum - ber my ba - by,

A la puerta del cielo (page 3)

slum - ber my ba - by, slum - ber my ba - by a - rru, a - rru.

GRADE 4

Li'l 'Liza Jane

American Dance-Game Song
Arranged by Marilyn Copeland Davidson

Li'l 'Liza Jane (page 2)

Li'l 'Liza Jane (page 3)

Voice: Oh, E - li - za, Li'l 'Li - za Jane.

Descant: Oh, E - li - za, E - li - za Jane!

Allundé, Alluia

Melody based on a Nigerian Harvest Song
As sung and arranged by
Margaret Campbelle-Holman

GRADE 4

I'll Rise When the Rooster Crows

Appalachian Folk Song
As Sung by Uncle Dave Macon
Arranged by Carol King

I'll Rise When the Rooster Crows (page 2)

go-ing down south where the sun shines hot, Down where the su-gar cane grows.

Cedar Swamp

Appalachian Folk Song
Arranged by Robert de Frece

Cedar Swamp (page 2)

Swing a la - dy up and down, Swing a la - dy home,_____

Swing a la - dy up and down, Swing a la - dy home.

12

Cotton-Eye Joe

Tennessee Folk Song
Arranged by Carol King

'Most Done Ling'rin' Here

African American Spiritual
Arranged by Robert de Frece

If you get there be - fore I do, 'Most done ling - 'rin' here. Look

out for me I am com - in' too, 'Most done ling - 'rin' here.

14

'Most Done Ling'rin' Here (page 2)

Sail Away, Ladies

Mountain Dance
Arranged by Thom Borden

Ain't no_ use to sit and cry; Sail a-way, la-dies, sail a-way;

You'll be an an-gel by and by. Sail a-way, la-dies, sail a-way.

Sail Away, Ladies (page 2)

O•8

Water Come a Me Eye

Jamaican Calypso Song
Arranged by Robert de Frece

18

GRADE 4

Water Come a Me Eye (page 2)

Love Somebody

American Folk Song
Arranged by Thom Borden

20

Love Somebody (page 2)

Night Herding Song

Oh say, lit-tle do-gies, quit rov-ing a-round. You've wan-dered and tram-pled all

22

Night Herding Song (page 2)

Voice: o - ver the ground. Oh, graze a - long, do - gies, and move kind - a slow. And

Night Herding Song (page 3)

Voice: don't be for - ev - er so much on the go. Move slow, lit - tle do - gies, move

slow. _____ Hi – o, hi – o ___ hi – o. _____

Achshav
(Now)

Israeli Folk Song
Arranged by Margaret Campbelle-Holman

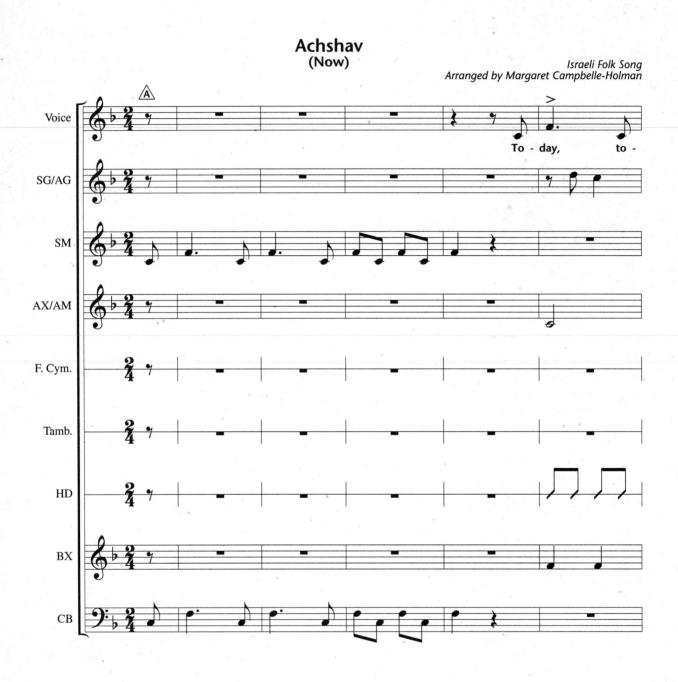

To - day, to -

GRADE 4

The B section lyrics: "land of Is-ra-el. Tum-ba, tum-ba, tum-ba, the land of Is-ra-"

Use Temple blocks instead of Hand Drums during B section

Achshav (page 4)

Voice: el, Hey! Tum-ba, tum-ba, tum-ba, the land of Is - ra - el. el.

Old Ark's A-Moverin'

African American Spiritual
Arranged by Robert de Frece

Old Ark's a - mov - er - in', a - mov - er - in', a - mov - er - in'. The

(No - ah's on the ark sail - ing.)

(Get on board the ark.)

Fine

Old Ark's a - mov - er - in' and I'm go - in' home.

Old Ark's A-Moverin' (page 2)

Bamboo Flute

Collected by Kathy B. Sorensen
English Words by Linda Worsley
Arranged by Virginia Nylander Ebinger

GRADE 4

Bamboo Flute (page 2)

Bamboo Flute (page 3)

Voice: You can make it sing, Put it to your mouth, let the mu-sic ring.

Bamboo Flute (page 4)

Bamboo Flute (page 5)

Voice: What will it play? "Vi di vi di" hear the song._____

Chicka Hanka

Track Laborer's Song
Arranged by Robert de Frece

Chicka Hanka (page 2)

GRADE 4

Roll on, Columbia

Music based on "Goodnight Irene"
by Huddie Ledbetter and John Lomax
Words by Woody Guthrie
Arranged by Virginia Nylander Ebinger

Roll on, Columbia (page 2)

moun - tains   and can - yons she   flew.   Ca - na - di - an

Roll on, Columbia (page 3)

Roll on, Columbia (page 4)

Roll on, Columbia (page 5)

Voice: on. Roll on,_____ Co - lum - bia, roll

Roll on, Columbia (page 6)

Voice: on. Your pow - er is turn - ing our dark - ness to

Roll on, Columbia (page 7)

When I Was Young

Irish Folk Song
Arranged by Marilyn Copeland Davidson

When I was young, I had no sense, I bought a fid-dle for

When I Was Young (page 2)

Voice: eigh - teen pence. The on - ly tune that I could play was o - ver the hills and

SG/AG

AM

AX

WB

BX

BM

When I Was Young (page 3)

Voice: ve - ry far a - way, so ear - ly in the morn - ing, so ear - ly in the

When I Was Young (page 4)

morn-ing,   so   ear-ly in   the morn-ing,   be-fore the break of   day.

Katyusha

Russian Folk Song
Arranged by Marilyn Copeland Davidson

Bloom - ing were the ap - ple and the pear trees,

Swirl - ing o'er the riv - er was the mist.

GRADE 4

Katyusha (page 2)

Walk in the Parlor

North Carolina Folk Song
Arranged by Robert de Frece

GRADE 4

Walk in the Parlor (page 2)

Johnson Boys

Appalachian Fiddle Tune
Arranged by Thom Borden

John-son boys they went a-court-in', John-son boys they did-n't stay; The rea-son why they did-n't stay, Had no mon-ey for to pay their way.

GRADE 4

Sea Shell

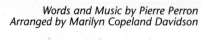

Page's Train

North Carolina Folk Song
Arranged by Marilyn Copeland Davidson

Pa - ge's train runs so fast,

Can't see noth - ing but the win - dow glass.

GRADE 4

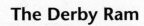

The Derby Ram

English Folk Song (Ozark Version)
Arranged by Marilyn Copeland Davidson

The Derby Ram (page 2)

Refrain

Voice: there I saw the fin - est ram that's ev - er fed on hay.____ And

AM: (Tell one, tell all, tell tall tales.)

AX: (Tell - ing to one, tell - ing to all, tell - ing a tall tale.)

The Derby Ram (page 3)

The Derby Ram (page 4)

GRADE 4

Who's Got a Fishpole?

American Folk Song
Arranged by Marilyn Copeland Davidson

Old Paint

American Folk Song
Arranged by Mary Goetze
and Marilyn Copeland Davidson

Good - bye, Old Paint, I'm a - leav - in' Chey - enne. Good -

bye, Old Paint, I'm a - leav - in' Chey - enne. I'm a -

GRADE 4

Old Paint (page 2)

Himmel und Erde
(Music Alone Shall Live)

German Round
Words Adapted by MMH
Arranged by Marilyn Copeland Davidson

All things will per - ish be neath___ the sky,

Mu - sic a - lone shall live. Mu - sic a - lone shall live,

64

Himmel und Erde (page 2)

¿Quién es ese pajarito?
(Who Is That Little Bird?)

Argentine Folk Song
English Words by Linda Worsley
Arranged by Marilyn Copeland Davidson

Voice: Who is that lit - tle bird sing - ing?

SG/AG: *(Please,* *please will you* *stop!)*

AM: *(Please,* *please,* *please* *you must stop!* *Won't you)*

AX: *(Please stop the song* *please stop the song,* *please* *stop)*

Shaker: *(Please,* *please,* *please* *stop)*

Drum: *(Please stop!* *Oh,)*

BX: *(Please,* *please,* *please.)*

¿Quién es ese pajarito? (page 2)

¿Quién es ese pajarito? (page 3)

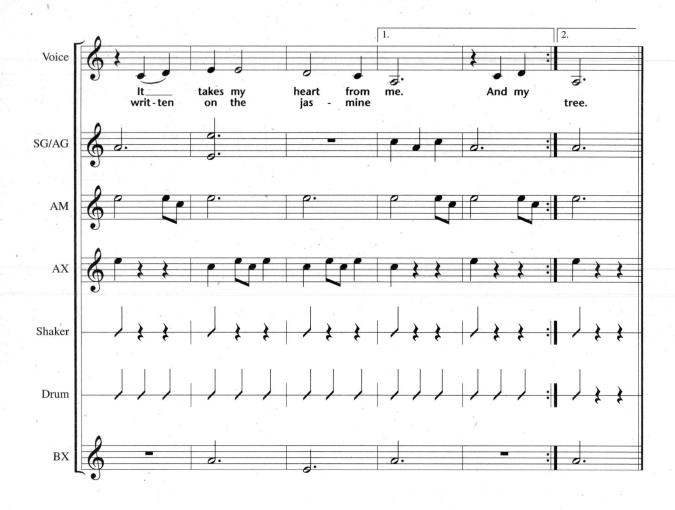

Voice: It___ takes my heart from me. And my
writ-ten on the jas - mine tree.